KATHERINE AND HUGH COLLEDGE

SHOOTING STARS

21 PIECES FOR VIOLIN PLAYERS

BOOSEY & HAWKES

Shooting Stars is the fourth book in a progressive series preceded by *Stepping Stones*, *Waggon Wheels* and *Fast Forward*. The 21 pieces concentrate on 01–2–3–4 and 01–2–34 finger patterns and include the augmented 2nd between the 1st and 2nd fingers. Triplets, basic syncopation and chromaticism are introduced, together with some new bowings and a piece in five time.

The pieces are grouped together in finger patterns and are not necessarily in order of difficulty.

KATHERINE & HUGH COLLEDGE
London, UK

Kathy and Hugh met in East London where they both worked as peripatetic teachers at Newham Academy of Music. Hugh had previously studied oboe and piano at Trinity College London while Kathy was a violin student at NE Essex Technical College (now Colchester Institute). They were both born in London but Kathy started to play the violin in New Zealand where she lived in her youth.

Their association with Boosey and Hawkes began in the 1980s when the couple added to the pieces Kathy had written for her pupils in Newham to create *Stepping Stones* and *Waggon Wheels*. They later added *Fast Forward* and *Shooting Stars*, as well as a number of works for beginner string ensemble in the *Simply 4 Strings* series. More recently they contributed two new string quartets to the *4 Strings* series edited by Liz Partridge.

They moved to Norfolk in 1995 and continued to teach in the State and Independent sectors until their retirement.

Published by Boosey & Hawkes Music Publishers Ltd
Aldwych House
71–91 Aldwych
London
WC2B 4HN

www.boosey.com

© Copyright 2021 by Boosey & Hawkes Music Publishers Ltd

ISMN 979-0-060-13833-1 | ISBN 978-1-78454-652-6 (violin part)
ISMN 979-0-060-13547-7 | ISBN 978-1-78454-471-3 (violin part & piano accompaniment)

Printed by Halstan:
Halstan UK, 2–10 Plantation Road, Amersham, Bucks, HP6 6HJ. United Kingdom
Halstan DE, Weißliliengasse 4, 55116 Mainz. Germany

Piano performance and audio production by Robin Bigwood
Violin performance by Alexandra Wood

Music origination by Moira Roach

Cover illustrations by Jo Moore
Cover design by Chloë Alexander Design

The original edition of this book was dedicated to the string players at
St Angela's Ursuline Convent School, Forest Gate, London Borough of Newham.

SHOOTING STARS

21 PIECES FOR VIOLIN PLAYERS

AUDIO RESOURCES

Stream or download audio for this book via the weblink below
or scan the QR code

https://audio.boosey.com/BxJK

1. The old oak tree

2. Head-in-the-clouds

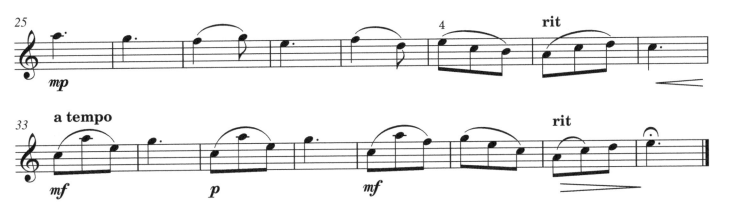

3. Morris dancers (for T.C. and 'The Lobster Potties' dancers of Sheringham)

4. The carol singers

Cheerfully

5. Cakewalk

Fairly fast

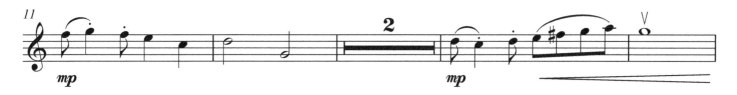

6. Alla marcia

In the style of a march

7. The misty isle

8. Carefree

9. Thingummyjig!

Lively, in the style of a jig

10. Five-a-side

Steadily (♪ = 168)

11. Chinatown

Moderato

12. Where the heather grows

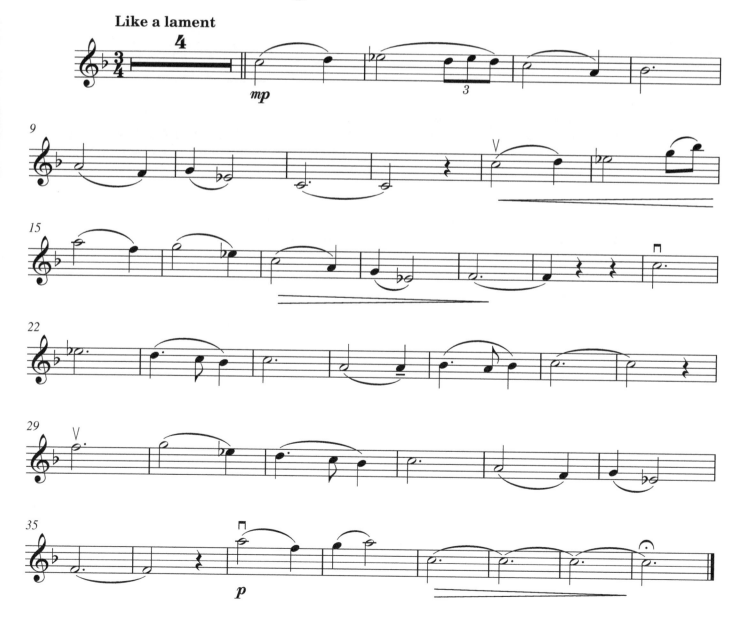

13. By candlelight

14. Coconuts and mangoes

15. Rustic dance

16. Far from home

17. Winter wind

18. **Look lively!**

19. Moto perpetuo

Allegro ma non troppo

20. Cossacks (for Adam, Anastasia and Seneaih)

21. Stiffkey blues

Stiffkey (sometimes pronounced 'Stookey') is a village in Norfolk, England.
'Stiffkey Blues' is a local seafood dish.